Thank you...

... for purchasing this copy of Writing for Literacy for ages 9-10. We hope that you find our worksheets, teachers' notes and display materials helpful as part of your programme of literacy activities.

This Writing for Literacy book is part of our growing range of educational titles. Most of our books are individual workbooks but, due to popular demand, we are now introducing a greater number of photocopiable titles especially for teachers. You may like to look out for:

WRITING FOR LITERACY for ages 5-7, 7-8, 8-9, 10-11

SPELLING FOR LITERACY for ages 5-7, 7-8, 8-9, 9-10, 10-11

READING FOR LITERACY for ages 5-7, 7-8, 8-9, 9-10, 10-11

NUMERACY TODAY for ages 5-7, 7-9, 9-11

HOMEWORK TODAY for ages 7-8, 8-9, 9-10, 10-11

To find details of our other publications, please visit our website: **www.acblack.com**

Andrew Brodie Publications

Suggestions for using this book ...

We have examined carefully the current national policies for teaching literacy. In writing this book we have included activities at **word level**, **sentence** level and **text level**, to be used as part of your programme of teaching. Within the teachers' notes we have provided some guidance as to extra resources that you may wish to use.

We have created thirty units of work that can be used at your discretion across the school year, though we have indicated a suggested term for each unit. To enable you to incorporate the units effectively into your teaching we make suggestions as to other materials that work well with our activities - particular traditional tales, for example.

Each unit consists of four sheets:

Sheet A consists of teachers' notes, providing full guidance for the three activi
sheets. Extra resources you may need are also listed here.
As you may well choose to use the unit as part of your programme of
activities we also provide a box for you to list other ideas, ready for n
time you use the unit.

Sheet B is the first activity sheet for each unit. It frequently includes detailed
instructions for other activities within the unit and can be photocopie
for use on an Overhead Projector or pinned to the wall as a reminder.

Sheet C often features text level work, though may well include word level or
sentence level activities.

Sheet D provides the culmination for each unit and, in some units, includes a
frame for extended writing.

We also include some extra writing frames at the very end of the book.

The publishers gratefully acknowledge the use of the following poems:

Sampan, Anon.; To a Mouse, Robert Burns; Topsy-Turvy World, William Brighty Rands; What a Heavy?, Christina Rossetti; Comparisons, Christina Rossetti; A Riddle, Christina Rossetti; Flint, Christina Rossetti; Gardening Lore, Juliana Ewing; The story of Johnny Head-in-Air, Heinrich Hoffman; From a Railway Carriage, Robert Louis Stevenson; The Land of the Counterpane, Rob Louis Stevenson.

We have attempted to contact all copyright holders for permission to use these works. We woul pleased if any copyright holders, not hereby acknowledged, could contact us.

Contents ...

Term 1

Term 2

Unit 11	B	Booklet frame for writing a myth or fable
	C	Other side of booklet frame
	D	Instructions for use of Sheets B and C

Unit 12	B	Instructions for revising and editing work
	C	'Notepad' for ideas about updating previous work
	D	Frame for presenting updated piece of work

Unit 13	B	Instructions for compiling a class anthology
	C	Writing frame for presenting chosen poems
	D	Frame for explanation of choice of poem

Unit 14	B	Poem for reading and discussion: 'Sampan'
	C	Further discussion and introduction of 'onomatopoeia'
	D	Frame for presentation of completed poem

Unit 15	B	'To a mouse': poem, information on Robert Burns and questions
	C	Worksheet on dialects
	D	Writing frame for presentation of poem written in a dialect

Unit 16	B	Revision of writing notes
	C	Presenting notes for others to read
	D	Use of others' notes to produce a mini-talk

Unit 17	B	'Buy-A-Home Property Sales': estate agent's details
	C	Instructions for writing new estate agent details
	D	Writing frame for presenting finished details

Unit 18	B	Instructions for writing acknowledgements
	C	Frame for presenting work based on history being studied
	D	Frame for acknowledgements

Unit 19	B	Instructions for evaluating own work
	C	Writing frame for evaluating others' work
	D	Frame for evaluating own work

Unit 20	B	Introduction to technical vocabulary
	C	'Notepad' for collecting technical vocabulary
	D	Building a class dictionary of technical vocabulary

© Andrew Brodie Publications ✓ www.acblack.com

Term 3

● **Teachers' Notes**

✓   This unit includes work on the text level requirements to record views, reflections and predictions about a book, and to show the development and structure of a book.

✓   **Resources**   Suitable fiction books to match the task.
You may wish pupils to complete this task using individual reading books, or you may wish the whole of a group or class to use the same book.
This task will be completed over a period of several lessons.

✓   **Sheet B**   An instructional sheet suitable for class or group use.
It is important that the reading material chosen is divided into five manageable pieces before beginning the task.
It is of course possible, for longer texts, to give each child two copies of Sheet C and split the book into up to ten sections.

✓   **Sheet C**   This is a five section writing frame for children to record their ideas on five separate occasions.

✓   **Sheet D**   A writing frame for children to reflect on the structure of the complete book.

Use this box to write your own notes ready for the next time you use this unit.

Name: Date:

Read these instructions carefully.

✐ You are going to read a book that you have not read before.

✐ Divide it into five sections of about the same length.

✐ After you have read each section you will be ready to fill in a section of Sheet C.

✐ In each section of Sheet C you should write about what you think of the characters and the story line, whether you are enjoying the book and, if so, why. If you did not enjoy that section of the book you should explain what you did not like about it. Also include your predictions about what you think will happen next.

✐ When you have completed the book you will be ready to reflect on it, and to fill in Sheet D.

✐ Use Sheet D to map out the story line of the book. You may want to use a simple chart or flow diagram to do this.

✐ Write down what you consider the high and low points of the book to be.

✐ Write about how you think the chapters of the book were linked, and whether you think those links were effective.

✐ If the book you read was the same one as others in your class, it will be interesting to compare your views with those of your class mates.

✐ Most importantly…   … enjoy your writing.

● **Text level work**

Name: _____   Date: _____

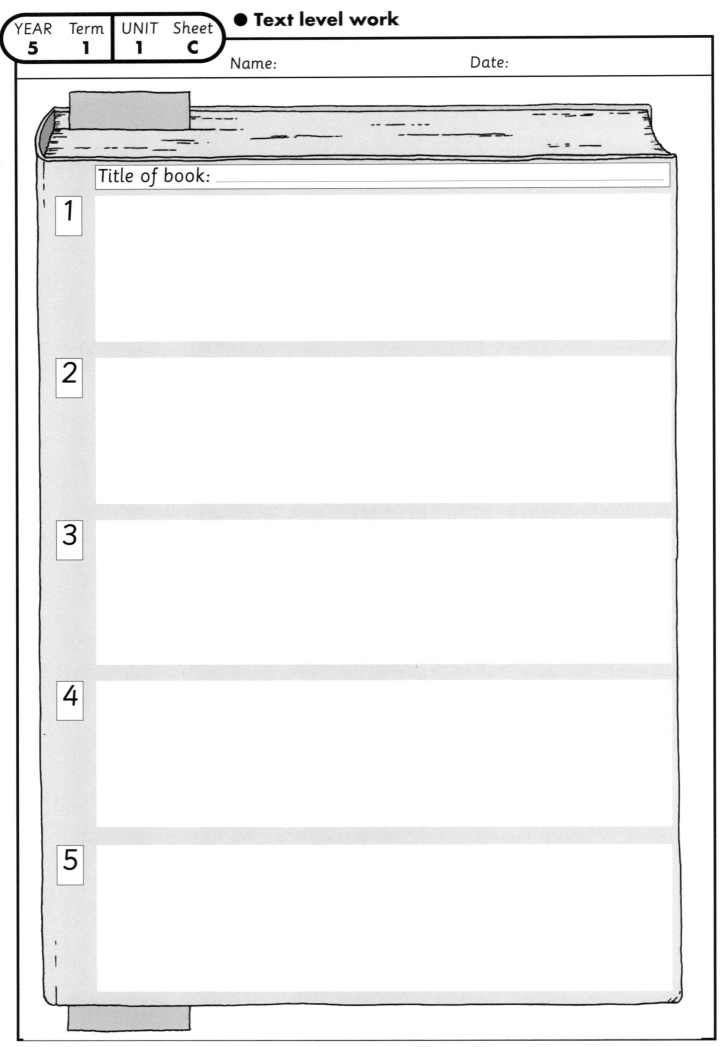

Title of book: _____

1

2

3

4

5

Name: Date:

Title of book: _____

Plot outline	

High points of book	

Low points of book	

How chapters are linked	

Overall opinion of book	

● Teachers' Notes

✓ In addition to sentence level work on writing dialogue, this unit includes a text level task on writing a new scene into a story.

✓ **Resources** A suitable fiction text. This may be the book that pupils have used for their work in Unit 1.
Examples of written dialogue.

✓ **Sheet B** An instructional sheet suitable for group use. It asks pupils to construct a new chapter to insert into a known book. Another option, or extension task, would be to use the existing story, but to create a new character to go into it.

✓ **Sheet C** A writing frame to use for the completion of the task. The frame has page number space at the bottom to allow for those pupils who choose to do so to write a lengthy chapter.

✓ **Sheet D** Includes both instructions and a writing frame for constructing a brief dialogue.

Use this box to write your own notes ready for the next time you use this unit.

Name: Date:

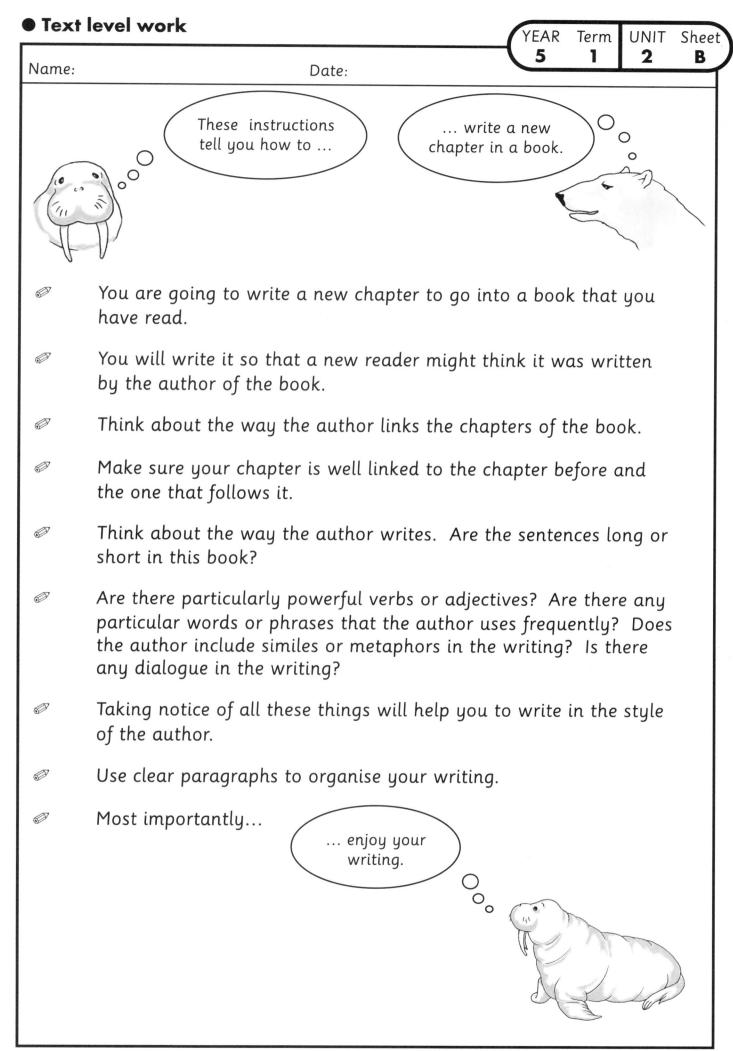

These instructions tell you how to …

… write a new chapter in a book.

You are going to write a new chapter to go into a book that you have read.

You will write it so that a new reader might think it was written by the author of the book.

Think about the way the author links the chapters of the book.

Make sure your chapter is well linked to the chapter before and the one that follows it.

Think about the way the author writes. Are the sentences long or short in this book?

Are there particularly powerful verbs or adjectives? Are there any particular words or phrases that the author uses frequently? Does the author include similes or metaphors in the writing? Is there any dialogue in the writing?

Taking notice of all these things will help you to write in the style of the author.

Use clear paragraphs to organise your writing.

Most importantly…

… enjoy your writing.

● **Text level work**

Name: Date:

● Sentence level work

Name: Date:

Choose two of the characters from a book that you have read recently.

Write a short dialogue that they would have been likely to have.

Consider whether the characters are friends or enemies.

Remember to begin a new line for each new speaker.

If a sentence begins before the direct speech, remember to put a comma before the speech marks.

Use words other than 'said' to ensure your dialogue is as interesting as possible.

Write your dialogue in the box below.

Most importantly …

… enjoy your writing.

● Teachers' Notes

✓ This unit covers text level work on the requirement to understand and write metaphors.

✓ **Resources** Any examples of metaphors.

✓ **Sheet B** This sheet briefly explains what a metaphor is. It asks pupils to pick out and illustrate the metaphors on the page.

✓ **Sheet C** This sheet gives a selection of metaphors about a house and asks pupils to add another and to illustrate them.

✓ **Sheet D** A frame in which pupils can write and illustrate a selection of metaphors about one subject of their choice. The frame is left blank to allow pupils the freedom to present this sheet as they would like to.

✓ In this unit we have used illustrations to emphasise the idea of one thing really being another!

Use this box to write your own notes ready for the next time you use this unit.

Name: Date:

✐ When we talk about a thing as though it is really something else we call it a **metaphor**.

Look, it's raining cats and dogs!

✐ Neatly cross out the phrase that is not **metaphorical**, and illustrate each metaphor.

My dad is a bear when he hugs me.

or

My dad runs like the wind.

The moon is as bright as a new penny.

or

The sun is a bicycle wheel with golden spokes.

The fire is a dragon.

or

The clouds are like candyfloss.

● **Text level work**

Name: _____ Date: _____

Illustrate these metaphors about a home.

Invent a 'home' metaphor of your own at the end.

My house is a blanket keeping me warm.

My bed is a bus that takes me to dreamland.

The windows are spectacles watching the neighbours.

_____

_____

_____

● Text level work

Name: Date:

✐   Write four or five metaphors about one topic in the frame below.

✐   Here are some possible topics:
    weather, an animal (of your choice), furniture.

✐   Illustrate your work to produce a thought-provoking, attractive
    result.

● Teachers' Notes

✓   This unit contains work on the text level requirement to write a poem expressing feelings.

✓   **Resources**   A range of poetry books, dictionaries and thesauruses.

✓   **Sheet B**   This is an instructional sheet suitable for class or group use.

✓   **Sheet C**   A writing frame for listing ideas from researching poetry for examples of suitable language.

✓   **Sheet D**   A writing frame for the presentation and possible display of final poems written.

Use this box to write your own notes ready for the next time you use this unit.

Name: Date:

What
is *sadness*?

It's when you feel
gloomy and miserable.

Writing Poetry About Feelings

✎   Many writers use poetry to effectively convey
feelings, moods and emotions to the reader.

✎   In this unit you are going to work on: 'happiness', 'sadness' and
'loneliness'.

✎   Find ideas in dictionaries, thesauruses, poetry books and other
books.

✎   Look for similes, metaphors and other figurative language.

✎   Try to find some interesting words that perhaps you have not used
before in your writing.

✎   You are going to write down some words that convey those
particular feelings.

✎   Your ideas can be written on Sheet C.

✎   Share your ideas with your classmates so that you can all add to
the ideas you have written.

✎   Next you are going to choose ONE of the themes you have worked
on as a basis for writing a poem of your own.

✎   Think of a good title for your poem.

✎   After you have written a first draft you will be able to revise and
improve your poem.

✎   Use Sheet D to present your finished work.

● **Text level work**

Name: _____   Date: _____

List all the interesting words and phrases you find …

…in the appropriate boxes.

<u>Happiness</u>

<u>Sadness</u>

<u>Loneliness</u>

Name: Date:

Present your completed poem below.

You may illustrate it if you wish.

● Teachers' Notes

✓ This unit contains work on the text level requirement to write a play script and annotate it for performance. This unit is closely linked to Unit 6, which concerns the evaluation of play scripts and performances.

✓ **Resources** Examples of play scripts.

✓ **Sheet B** An instructional sheet suitable for class or group use.
It is important to discuss the more effective ways of annotation that are in evidence in the resources you choose to use with the pupils.
For the purposes of this task it does not matter whether the pupils choose to write a play from a story they already know, or one of their own invention.
If there are much younger children in the school you may wish the children to write their plays for that audience.
This task can be completed by individuals, but works very well when done in pairs or small groups.

✓ **Sheet C** A writing frame for presentation of play scripts. Space for numbering is provided at the bottom of the page as it is likely that each play may be longer than one sheet.

✓ **Sheet D** This page is to encourage pupils to think about the importance of the positioning of their characters and how they might need to move around during the performance.

Use this box to write your own notes ready for the next time you use this unit.

Name: Date:

✎ You are going to write a short play. It will only have one scene and no more than four characters.

✎ Remember to use all that you know about how to present a play script.

✎ Include all the stage directions that are needed. You will need to do this in a way that ensures it cannot be muddled with the dialogue. This could include using brackets, writing in italics or even writing in a different colour ink.

✎ Draft your work first. Only write the finished work when you are completely happy with your play.

✎ Use Sheet C to present your completed play script.

✎ Use Sheet D to show where your characters will be positioned at the beginning of the play. You may wish to use arrows to show where they will need to move during the performance.

✎ You will be able to use Sheet D to write some instructions for the actions that will take place. These instructions are called 'stage directions'.

Now you are ready to perform your play.

● **Text level work**

Name: Date:

Present your
play here.

© Andrew Brodie Publications ✓ www.acblack.com

Name: Date:

● Teachers' Notes

✓ This unit is closely linked to Unit 5, and concerns the text level requirement to evaluate a play script and the performance of it.

✓ **Resources** The plays written by pupils for Unit 5.

✓ **Sheet B** This is an instructional sheet suitable for class or group use. It is important to consider the scripts alongside the performances.
As in Unit 5, this unit works well when tackled by groups. You may even wish to use Sheet C as a whole class sheet when listing views on each performance.
NB It is extremely important to encourage pupils to criticise constructively to ensure that this task is positive and meaningful. Every play script and performance should be valued. Ensure the children realise that every play will benefit from some changes however minor, and that this is just as important to the final product as is the revision and improvement of poetry.

✓ **Sheet C** This can be used to list points noted when considering the script and the performance. This can be used as a sheet for an individual or by a group. The latter usually proves to be particularly effective.

✓ **Sheet D** This sheet is similar to Sheet C in Unit 5, and is to be used to produce the revised script.

✓ Ideally this unit should be completed with performances of the revised plays in order that the improvements can be noted, discussed and valued.

Use this box to write your own notes ready for the next time you use this unit.

✎   You are going to perform your play for your classmates to evaluate.

✎   You, in turn, will evaluate the performances that you watch.

✎   When you are watching the play, think about the most effective parts of it, and the parts that could be changed.

✎   Is the story line clear?

✎   Do the characters use gestures and movement to help to keep the play interesting?

✎   After watching the play, you can list your comments on Sheet C.

✎   When you have received other people's comments about your play you can use Sheet D to revise it to produce an even better version.

Remember that criticism is most useful when it is constructive.

Name: Date:

Evaluate a play script and performance here.

List your points clearly.

Evaluation of _____

Name: Date:

Write your revised
script here.

Enjoy
performing it.

● Teachers' Notes

✓ This unit contains work on the text level requirement to recount the same event for both a known and an unknown reader.

✓ **Resources** Examples of holiday articles from magazines, newspapers or books.

✓ **Sheet B** This is an instructional sheet suitable for class or group use.

✓ **Sheet C** This writing frame is shown as the beginning of a letter - though, in this instance, without the address and date area at the top.

✓ **Sheet D** This writing frame is shown as if it is from a newspaper or magazine.

✓ Presenting the frames in this way serves as an effective reminder of the style of writing needed and provides a suitable vehicle for display purposes.

Use this box to write your own notes ready for the next time you use this unit.

In this unit you are going to consider different ways to write about the same occasion.

You are going to use Sheet C to write about the holiday or day out as if you are writing a letter to a good friend.

Your friend will probably know some or all of the people you were with.

When you write to a friend it looks rather like a conversation on paper!

You are going to use Sheet D to write a report for a newspaper or magazine about the same holiday or day out.

This piece of writing will be much more formal. The readers do not know you, your family or your friends. They will be interested in different parts of your holiday or day trip.

Discuss what you think the differences are most likely to be before you begin writing.

Plan each piece of writing carefully. A good way to begin is to write a simple diary about your trip so that you have everything sequenced correctly.

● **Text level work**

Name: Date:

Write to a
good friend.

Dear _____

_____

_____

_____

_____

_____

_____

_____

_____

_____

_____

_____

_____

_____

_____

_____

_____

with love from _____

Name: Date:

Remember to write a title for your article.

👡👡 Literacy News Holiday Supplement ☼

_____

● Teachers' Notes

✓ This unit tackles work on the text level requirement to write instructional texts, and to test them out. You may wish the pupils to design games to be played by their peers or by younger children. It is important that they know what age their game is aimed for as it will have an impact on the language they use when writing the instructions.

✓ **Resources** A selection of instructions for playing board games. These can be used to evaluate their presentation, clarity and completeness.

✓ **Sheet B** An instructional sheet suitable for class or group use. This sheet introduces the task and asks pupils to work in pairs or small groups, although you may wish children to work individually.
The game board has been designed to easily allow for movement up, down, right, left or following a spiral.

✓ **Sheet C** This is a game board. The ideal way to use this is to photocopy it in the original A4 format for game planning. Later the final game can be made by copying the sheet onto card. At this stage you may wish to enlarge the sheet to give a larger game playing surface.

✓ **Sheet D** This is a writing frame for presentation of the final version of the instructions for playing the game.
This frame is designed to be a little smaller than the game playing board so that it can be adhered to the reverse of it. Laminating the finished product for greater durability will allow the games produced to be put in use by the class.

Use this box to write your own notes ready for the next time you use this unit.

Name: Date:

You are going to design a new game.

Then you will write a clear set of instructions so that others can play it.

✐ Work with a partner or in a group of three.

✐ Use the game board on Sheet C as your game board.

✐ It is a fairly plain board, so you can decide if the spaces need to be numbered, or have designs or instructions on some of them.

✐ You could have a FINISH space somewhere in the middle, or at the top or the bottom. You could design many interesting ways to get there.

✐ You may wish to have a theme for your game. Perhaps a particular book, film or even a place that you know about.

✐ You may roll dice, turn over cards, or do something else altogether to find out how far to go, and in which direction.

✐ When you have designed a really good game you must write the game playing rules so that other people can enjoy your game too.

✐ Remember to sequence them correctly and number your instructions where appropriate. Include a list of items needed to play the game.

✐ Ask another group to test your game by following your instructions.

✐ They may be able to spot any instructions you may have forgotten to write.

✐ When you are completely happy with your game and the instructions, you will be able to complete a final version of the game board on a piece of card.

✐ Write the final version of the instructions in the frame on Sheet D.

● **Text level work**

Name: Date:

Use this frame ...

... for playing the game you invent.

Name: Date:

Write instructions for your game in the frame below.

● Teachers' Notes

✓ This unit contains work on the text level requirements to use simple abbreviations in note-taking, and to make notes for different purposes.

✓ **Resources** None needed, though any examples of common abbreviations would be helpful.

✓ **Sheet B** An instructional sheet suitable for class or group use.

✓ **Sheet C** A text for pupils to use to take notes from. They should be encouraged to write in note form and to use any abbreviations possible.
If time allows, it is beneficial to allow children to compare completed notes before tackling the final part of the task. Pupils will need their notes to complete the final part of the task, but they should NOT retain the original text.

✓ **Sheet D** This sheet asks children to answer a few questions about the text and to mark in the route the bus took on a map .

Use this box to write your own notes ready for the next time you use this unit.

Let's think of some ways of making note-taking easier.

✐ When you are taking notes from a book, or from a talk you are listening to, there are some ways of making the job easier.

✐ You can use the sign '&' instead of writing the word 'and'.

✐ Instead of writing whole sentences you can just use key words or phrases.

✐ Miss out any words that are not needed.

✐ Use mathematical signs in place of words where appropriate.

✐ Some words are easily abbreviated: 'Edn.' in place of education.

✐ Other words are often replaced by initial letters: 'R.A.F.' in place of Royal Air Force.

✐ Can you think of other ways of making note-taking easier? Share your ideas with your friends.

✐ The important thing is that you should be able to read your notes yourself so that you can do a piece of writing from them, or tell other people about what you have learned.

✐ Read the story on Sheet C, and use the space at the bottom of the page to convert the information into brief notes.

✐ See how brief you can make the notes without losing any of the meaning.

✐ You will only have up to ten minutes to complete this task.

● **Text level work**

Name: Date:

Mayhem on the School Bus

Yesterday afternoon there was confusion when a new driver was in charge of the school bus. It left Maysfield Primary School at 3.30.pm and should have arrived in the neighbouring village of Droxford at about 3.45pm.

The bus proceeded as normal along Green Road, but unfortunately the driver then took the third turning on the right which led him in the wrong direction completely. He went straight across the roundabout, demolishing two flower beds and six rose bushes, before going right again onto Wobbly Way. As the name of that road suggests, there are many bends along it, and before reaching the end three children had been very travel sick.

By this time the driver had begun to realise that he was not going towards Droxford and was getting rather anxious. After crossing the river the bus went along the road to the right, known as Church Lane. On reaching the next junction the driver went straight on into School Road. Two minutes later an amazed and rather confused driver discovered that he had taken the school bus on a route that ended up back where it had started from.

Tomorrow the driver will study the map before he begins the trip.

Write your notes here.
Remember you only have 10 minutes.

You will need your notes to answer questions on the next sheet.

Name: Date:

Answer these questions and complete the map.

✳   What was the name of the school?

_____

✳   What time did the school bus leave?

_____

✳   Where was it going?

_____

✳   What will the driver need to do before he drives the bus tomorrow?

_____

✎   Now mark the route the bus took, on the map below.

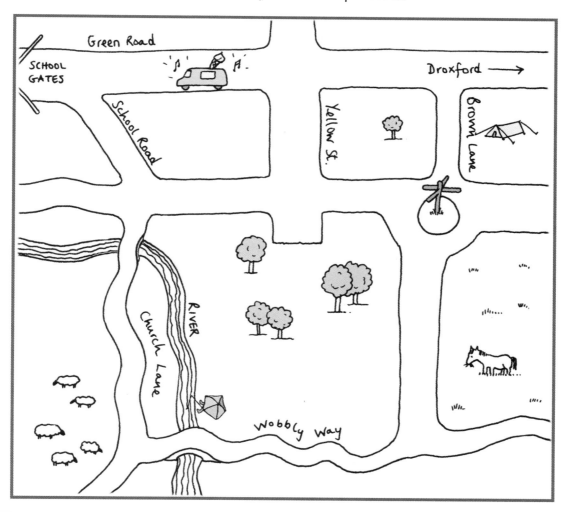

● **Teachers' Notes**

✓ This unit concerns the text level requirement to make notes for different purposes. It is designed so that it can be used more than once by the same group of pupils as a starting point for different types of writing. The final outcome each time will depend on the type of text that is read to the pupils.

✓ **Resources** Texts for reading aloud to pupils. These might include informational texts linked to other curriculum areas being taught, newspaper articles, other topical information or items of local interest.

Suitable ideas for this unit include:

1) Information about an event being presented as a poster.
2) An article about a site of historical interest being presented as a guide sheet for visitors.
3) A newspaper article concerning an item of public debate, being presented as a script for a speech that is either for or against the idea or proposal.
4) Geographical or historical information being presented as an illustrated wall chart or informational text .
5) A talk about a recent sporting event being presented as a newspaper report.

There are of course many other possibilities.

✓ **Sheet B** An instructional sheet suitable for class or group use.

✓ **Sheet C** This is a writing frame presented as a notebook, as a visual reminder that pupils need only to take notes, rather than attempt to produce flowing prose.

✓ **Sheet D** A writing frame for the presentation of a final piece of writing that has been developed from the notes taken.

Use this box to write your own notes ready for the next time you use this unit.

Name: Date:

You are going to write notes ...

... from listening to someone speaking.

☛ Your teacher is going to read to you, and you are going to take notes during the reading.

☛ You will need to use abbreviations, and key words or phrases.

☛ You will not be able to write down every word spoken.

☛ Only write what you need to write to help you remember what has been said.

☛ Do not worry if you cannot spell a word you need to know. If you can read it afterwards then that is all that really matters, though later it would be a good idea to check it in a dictionary.

☛ Your teacher will not be able to stop and repeat things, so it is important to listen carefully whilst the reading is going on.

☛ You will be given two minutes after the reading is finished to add anything to your notes while the content of the talk is still fresh in your memory. You will not be able to talk to anyone else during this time.

☛ Use Sheet C to jot your notes on.

✎ After you have made your notes, your teacher will tell you what sort of writing they are to be used for.

✎ You may be asked to write a newspaper report, an information text for a particular audience, an advertising poster, a fact sheet or even the script for a speech.

✎ Plan your work carefully before presenting your final version on Sheet D.

● **Text level work**

Name: Date:

Write your notes here.

Now spend 2 minutes quietly adding anything else you still remember but did not get time to write down.

● Text level work

Name: Date:

● Teachers' Notes

✓ This unit contains work on the text level requirement to investigate legends, fables and myths.

✓ **Resources** A selection of well-known myths, legends and fables for pupils to read and discuss. It is important that children understand the difference between these forms of traditional story.

✓ **Sheet B** Provides a definition of a legend and gives the story of Robin Hood as an example.

✓ **Sheet C** Provides a definition of a myth. The story of Daedalus and Icarus is used as an example of a Greek myth.

✓ **Sheet D** Provides a definition of a fable and refers to Aesop's famous fable of the Hare and the Tortoise.

✓ Having observed the distinction between myths, legends and fables, the children should be asked to choose one to rewrite in their own words. We suggest that they use a plain piece of paper with a line guide paper-clipped to it. Line guide templates are provided at the end of the book.

Use this box to write your own notes ready for the next time you use this unit.

Name: Date:

What is a legend?

It's a story that might be partly true but nobody really knows the whole truth.

Legends are traditional stories, handed down from generation to generation. One of the most famous is the Legend of Robin Hood.

❖ Find out what you can about Robin Hood:

❖ When did he live?

❖ Where did he live?

❖ Who was the king at the time?

❖ Who were Robin Hood's enemies?

❖ Who was his lady friend?

❖ Can you find the names of some of his other friends?

Write your notes on this sheet.

● **Text level work**

Name: Date:

What is a myth?

A traditional story but not usually based on real events.

A myth often features people or animals with **supernatural** powers.

Look up the word 'supernatural' in a dictionary. What does it mean?

_____

_____

_____

This is a character from a Greek myth. Can you find out who she is and what her supernatural powers are.

_____

_____

_____

Another Greek myth features Daedalus and Icarus. They were both able to fly. What happened to Icarus on his flight?

_____

_____

_____

You should be able to think of a modern story where somebody is able to fly. Why is this story not a myth?

_____

_____

Name: Date:

What is a fable?

A fable is rather like a myth but it often features animals and there is usually a moral to the story.

Fables written by a man called Aesop are very famous. One of his stories is 'The Hare and The Tortoise'. Write out the main points of the story.

_____

_____

_____

_____

_____

_____

_____

_____

_____

_____

_____

What is the moral of the story?

_____

_____

_____

_____

Enjoy your writing.

 **Teachers' Notes**

✓   This unit covers the text level requirement to revise work to match it to the needs of a particular reader. For the purposes of this unit pupils are asked to revise a piece of writing produced for the previous unit to make it suitable for a six year-old.

✓   **Resources**   Examples of fiction for Year One children. If possible samples of myths, fables or legends produced for use at Key Stage One would be ideal.
Focus on the use of language, presentation, illustrations, etc.

✓   **Sheet B**   An instructional sheet suitable for class or group use.

✓   **Sheet C**   This is designed for pupils to write down ideas of the changes they may need to make when revising their writing. It is important to allow time for these notes to be discussed.

✓   **Sheet D**   A frame to be used for the presentation of the revised pieces of writing. You may wish to supply pupils with guidelines with a 15 mm. space between lines.
If you have Year One children in school the final pieces of writing could be 'tested' by them.

Use this box to write your own notes ready for the next time you use this unit.

Name: Date:

You are going to learn about revising and editing work …

… to make it suitable for a particular type of reader.

✎   To complete this unit you will need to use a myth, legend or fable that you wrote as part of the last unit.

✎   You are going to change your work so that it would be suitable for a six year-old to read and enjoy.

✎   Sheet C is for you to jot notes about the changes you think you may need to make.

✎   Think about the sort of vocabulary that a Year One pupil would understand and be able to read.

✎   Make sure that you write in clear simple sentences.

✎   Not many six year-olds read joined writing easily, so you will need to print clearly, or use a word processor.

✎   Some of the details of the setting of the story may need to be in the illustrations rather than the text.

- -

✎   When you have written notes about the changes you may need to share your ideas with a friend. Your friend may help you with other ideas. Be prepared to help a friend by discussing their story with them too.

✎   Sheet D is for the presentation of your final story. There is a page numbering space at the bottom of the page in case you need more than one sheet.

✎   The very best way to see whether your work has been successful is to allow a six year-old to read it. You will soon know whether your work has been revised well if it is tested in this way.

● **Text level work**

Name: Date:

Use the writing you did in Unit 11.

How can you make it suitable for a six year-old?

✎ Write your ideas here.

Discuss your ideas with a friend.

● Text level work

Name: Date:

✐ Write your revised story here.

● **Teachers' Notes**

✓ This unit covers the text level requirement to compile a class anthology of favourite poems, and to include reasons for the choices.
Unlike other units in this publication, this requirement is taken from the reading comprehension element of the literacy strategy. This is due to the practical written nature of this particular requirement.

✓ **Resources** This unit builds on the requirement to understand terms that describe different kinds of poems, so there should be a wide variety of poems for pupils to read, discuss and enjoy. These poems should be by many different poets from differing eras. When tackling this unit it would be ideal if each pupil could choose a different poem.

✓ **Sheet B** An instructional sheet suitable for class or group use.

✓ **Sheet C** This is a writing frame for the presentation of chosen poems. We have incorporated a 'watermark' of pictures that pupils can write over. They should add their own pictures relevant to the poem that they are using.

✓ **Sheet D** This frame is for pupils to write about the reasons for the choices made.

Use this box to write your own notes ready for the next time you use this unit.

Name: Date:

You are going to help to make a class **anthology**.

An **anthology** is a collection of poems.

✎ You are going to choose a poem that you particularly like.

✎ It may be by any poet.

✎ Sheet C is for you to present the poem on.

✎ Write as neatly as you can.

✎ Present the poem with care, and illustrate it if you wish to.

✎ The title of the poem should go on the title line at the top of Sheet C.

✎ You may need to use guidelines behind the paper to help to keep your work neat.

✎ The lines at the bottom of the sheet are for the name of the poet who wrote the poem, and for your name as the copier and illustrator.

✎ Sheet D is also for you to write on.

✎ You are going to write about why you have chosen that particular poem.

✎ Include details about how the poem makes you feel, what you like about the language used and any other details that will help the reader to understand your reasons for choosing the poem.

✎ When all the poems chosen by people in your class are displayed or put into a class book, with of course the reasons for the choices, you will have a wonderful anthology to share and enjoy.

● **Text level work**

Name: _____   Date: _____

My Favourite Poem

_____

by _____

Copied and Illustrated by _____

Name: Date:

Remember to write interesting details …

… explaining your choice of poem.

Why _____

is my favourite poem.

● Teachers' Notes

✓ This unit (like the next) is based on the text level requirement to use the structures of poems read as a basis for own writing. It also helps to fulfil the word level requirement to explore onomatopoeia.

✓ **Resources** Poems showing ways of using onomatopoeia.

✓ **Sheet B** This sheet asks pupils to read and discuss the poem SAMPAN.
At this point pupils have not been introduced to the idea that the unit has a particular focus on onomatopoeia, and can discuss all the features they notice about it.

✓ **Sheet C** This sheet continues from the previous one and introduces the idea of using onomatopoeia.
At the bottom of the page they are asked to write a poem with the same structure as SAMPAN and with clear use of onomatopoeia. It is important to make it clear that this poem may have a completely different subject matter. Lower ability pupils may find it more difficult to work within the confines of the structure and the onomatopoeia, and for these pupils you may wish to focus on just one of these items.

✓ **Sheet D** A writing frame for the presentation of the final versions of pupils' own poems.

Use this box to write your own notes ready for the next time you use this unit.

● **Text level work**

Name: Date:

Read this poem.

Why do you think it says 'Anon.' at the bottom?

Sampan

Waves lap lap,
Fish fins clap clap,
Brown sails flap flap,
Chopsticks tap tap.

Up and down the long green river,
Oh hey, oh hey, lanterns quiver.
Willow branches brush the river,
Oh hey, oh hey, lanterns quiver.

Chopsticks tap tap,
Brown sails flap flap,
Fish fins clap clap,
Waves lap lap.

Anon.

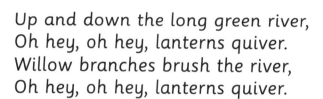

What features of this writing make it obvious that it is a poem?

© Andrew Brodie Publications ✓ www.acblack.com

● **Word and text level work**

Name: Date:

Did you enjoy the poem on the previous sheet?

✎ You should have noticed a number of features that told you that the writing was a poem.

✎ Among them you will have seen onomatopoeia.

✎ **Onomatopoeia** is the use of words that sound like what they are describing. Words like 'hiss', 'tap' and 'splash' are common examples of onomatopoeia.

✎ Use the space below to jot down some more words that work in this way.

✎ Use the next space to incorporate some of those words into short poetic phrases.

✎ Use the writing frame on Sheet D to write a poem with the same structure as SAMPAN. Make sure you use some onomatopoeia as that is a very important feature of the poem you have just read.

Name: Date:

Carefully present
your poem here.

● Teachers' Notes

✓ This unit, like the last, concerns the text level requirement to write poetry based on poems that the children have read.

✓ **Resources** Examples of poems written in dialects, and/or poetry written by Robert Burns. You may particularly wish to show pupils the whole of the poem 'To a Mouse', and allow pupils to investigate the life and work of Robert Burns.

✓ **Sheet B** This sheet has the first verse of the poem 'To A Mouse' by Robert Burns.
The sheet also has a little information about the poet and some questions for pupils to consider.

✓ **Sheet C** This sheet introduces the idea of writing a poem in a local dialect. It is important to ensure that pupils understand the difference between an accent and a dialect.

✓ **Sheet D** A writing frame for the presentation of a poem written in dialect.

✓ Extra activity - you may wish pupils to make a glossary to accompany their poems.

As a starting point for this, the class may wish to try to make a mini glossary for 'To a Mouse'. This is also an ideal opportunity to introduce pupils to the variety of dictionaries that are available.

Use this box to write your own notes ready for the next time you use this unit.

Name: _____   Date: _____

See if you can read this poem.

It may make better sense if you read it aloud.

To a Mouse

Wee, sleekit, cowrin, tim'rous beastie,
O, what a panic's in thy breastie!
Thou need na start awa so hasty,
Wi bickering brattle
I wad be lath to rin an' chase thee,
Wi murd'ring pattle.

✸ That is the first verse of a poem by a poet called Robert Burns.

✸ He was born in 1759 and died at the age of only thirty-seven, in 1796.

✸ Robert Burns is extremely famous and is known as Scotland's national poet.

✸ He also wrote the words to a very well-known song that many people sing each New Year. Can you guess what that is?

✸ In Scotland there is a special night called Burns Night when many people read his poetry. Do you know the date of Burns Night?

✸ At first, the poem is very difficult to read. Here is a **glossary** to show what some of the words mean:

awa	away	rin	run
beastie	animal, beast	sleekit	smooth-furred
brattle	scamper	thee	you
breastie	chest	thou	you
cowrin	cowering, crouching in fear	thy	your
		tim'rous	timorous, frightened
lath	loath	wee	small
pattle	small spade with a long handle	wi	with

● **Text level work**

Name: Date:

> Did you understand what 'To a Mouse' was about?

✎ Robert Burns lived in Scotland and spoke a Scottish dialect.

✎ Do you know what a dialect is?

✎ In the box below write a definition for the word **dialect**.

✎ Think about the local dialect where you live or where you or your parents were born.

✎ Use the box below to write some words or phrases in that dialect. You may have to spell the words as they sound because they are not likely to be found in your dictionaries at school.

✎ Write a poem in the dialect you have chosen.

✎ The poem can be about whatever you choose and you can decide how to structure it.

✎ Ask a friend to read your poem aloud so that you can judge whether it sounds the way you intended it to.

✎ Present your finished poem in the writing frame on Sheet D.

✎ Write neatly and illustrate your poem with care.

Name: _____   Date: _____

● Teachers' Notes

✓   This unit covers work on the text level requirement to convert personal notes into notes that others can read.

✓   **Resources**   None needed to complete this unit.

✓   **Sheet B**   This sheet has both instructions and an area for writing notes. It asks pupils to write as many notes as possible about their own life in only five minutes. Hence the notes will have to be designed using abbreviations and key words that will serve as a reminder only to the writer of the notes.

✓   **Sheet C**   This sheet also contains instructions and a note writing area. It asks pupils to expand on their previous notes so that another pupil would understand them. Ten minutes is allowed for this task.

✓   **Sheet D**   This has brief instructions and a writing frame. The frame is to allow pupils to use the notes written by another pupil, to write a mini-talk about the life of that person. Pupils will be asked to imagine that they are introducing the pupil about whom they are writing as a famous author about to give a talk to an audience.

Use this box to write your own notes ready for the next time you use this unit.

● Text level work

Name: Date:

Try to remember all you know about writing brief notes.

✐ You are going to use the notepad on this page for writing very brief notes about your life.

✐ You need to include details such as your date and place of birth, where you live and with whom. No one but you will need to read these notes, so you can use any abbreviations that you will understand when you next need the notes.

✐ Your teacher will be timing this activity.

✐ You will only have five minutes to note down as much information as you can.

Write your notes on the notepad.

● **Text level work**

Name: Date:

✏ Now you are going to take the notes you made about yourself and rewrite them so that other people can understand them.

✏ You are still writing notes so you do not need to write in full sentences, but your notes should be easily understood by anyone who reads them.

✏ Later your teacher is going to give your notes to someone else in your class. That person is going to turn those notes into a short talk about you. They are going to imagine that you are an author and you have arrived at the town hall to give a talk about your work - they have to introduce you to the audience. Their introduction must tell the audience quite a lot about you.

✏ It is not your job to make your notes into a talk - someone else is going to have to do that.

✏ Remember not to add any extra notes to those you wrote before, just make the ones you already have easier to understand.

✏ You will only have ten minutes to complete this task.

Name: Date:

✐   You will be given someone else's notes.

✐   You are going to write a talk about them. Imagine that you have to introduce that person to a large hall full of people.

✐   You must work only from the notes. You will not be allowed to speak to the author of the notes or add any other things you know about them. You must pretend you have never met that person before.

✐   Later you may have the chance to read your talk to the class.

> Think about sequencing your talk in a sensible way. Begin with the birth date of your person.

● Teachers' Notes

✓　This unit concerns the text level requirement to write non-chronological texts in a clear, concise and impersonal style.

✓　**Resources**　It would be ideal if pupils were able to see a variety of estate agents' details of properties for sale.

✓　**Sheet B**　This sheet shows the sort of details that might be produced by an estate agent interested in selling a property.
It is important to discuss the language used, the structure of the very concise sentences and the presentation of the text.

✓　**Sheet C**　This is an instructional sheet concerning the task of writing estate agents' details of their own home, or another that they know well.

✓　**Sheet D**　This is a writing frame in which to produce details, in the style of an estate agent, for their chosen property.

Use this box to write your own notes ready for the next time you use this unit.

Name: Date:

Buy-A-Home Property Sales

Three bedroom village property.

Unique opportunity to buy a property in a quiet country village. This well-proportioned house is convenient for schools, public transport and shops and within easy reach of the coast. This house has the benefits of sealed unit double glazing and oil central heating.

Accommodation: Hall, Lounge, Dining room. Kitchen, Three Bedrooms, Bathroom, parking and large garden to the rear of the property.

Entrance hall: with radiator and stairs.

Lounge: 4.3m x 3.3m Open fireplace, radiators and French doors leading to garden.

Kitchen: 3.5m x 2.9m Fully fitted with oak fronted units and built in cooker and fridge. Hatch to dining room.

Dining room: 3.5m x 2.8m Fitted carpet, telephone point and radiator.

Stairs to upstairs landing and bedrooms.

Bedroom One: 4.3m x 3.3m Double aspect room with views over farmland.

Bedroom Two: 3.7m x 3.2m Fitted wardrobes, radiator.

Bedroom Three: 3.6m x 2.9m with radiator and fitted wardrobe.

Bathroom: This incorporates W.C. Basin, Bath, Heated towel rail and airing cupboard with hot water tank.

Don't delay - View today.

● **Text level work**

Name: Date:

> Now it is your turn to be an estate agent.

✎ Begin by discussing the property details on Sheet B. You may also have had the opportunity to look at some genuine estate agents' details in your area.

✎ Did you notice that the details on Sheet B had not been completed? That is because most details need at least two sides of an A4 sheet.

✎ In addition to the beginning of sentences and proper nouns, many estate agents put capital letters at the beginning of any words that they want a prospective customer to notice.

✎ There are many abbreviations that estate agents use. For instance SUDG is often used to save writing 'sealed unit double glazing'. This is done to save space as they have limited space to fit in all the details they wish to include.

✎ Make a list of all the abbreviations you can find in estate agents' property details.

✎ Have you also noticed that only the good things about a property are mentioned? You will never see 'Ugly house set far too close to busy and very dangerous road' written on estate agents' details. Why do you think that is?

✎ Think about your own home, or another one that you know very well.

✎ Use Sheet D to write about it as though you are an estate agent trying to sell it.

✎ Present the details in just the same way that an estate agent would.

✎ You may need to use the back of the sheet.

✎ Use the photograph space to draw and colour a picture of the home you are 'selling'. Make the picture as realistic as possible.

Name: Date:

Buy-A-Home Property Sales

Don't delay - View today.

● Teachers' Notes

✓ This unit contains work on the text level requirement for pupils to acknowledge sources in their own writing.

The unit has been designed to be used to teach literacy through other subjects. In this case history has been used as a vehicle for this work though it could be used equally successfully with other areas of the curriculum.

✓ **Resources** A range of books associated with the history topic currently being studied by the class.
These will be used to investigate the way sources are acknowledged.

✓ **Sheet B** An instructional sheet suitable for class or group use.

✓ **Sheet C** A frame on which pupils will present their work on an aspect of the history that they are studying.

✓ **Sheet D** This is a writing frame on which pupils can record their acknowledgements.

Use this box to write your own notes ready for the next time you use this unit.

* Look in a selection of history books to find the acknowledgements.

* The acknowledgements section is usually at the end of the book.

* All publishers are obliged to include these acknowledgements.

* Those acknowledgements might refer to other publications, pictures, museums or people.

* Look at the order in which each publication has recorded its acknowledgements.

* When you are asked to find out about something and write about it, you too should record your acknowledgements.

* Your acknowledgements should include the title and publisher of any book you have used, as well as the names of any people who have been able to give you information.

* If you are learning about the history of your locality, and an elderly person has been able to tell you about it from personal experience, it is important to thank them in your acknowledgements.

✏ Your teacher is going to ask you to find out and write about an aspect of the history topic you are studying at the moment.

✏ You will use Sheet C to present your work.

✏ You will use Sheet D to record your acknowledgements.

✏ When you are doing your research, note the details of the sources you are using as you go along.

✏ Record your acknowledgements in a logical order.

● **Text level work**

Name: Date:

Use this frame to present your history work.

● **Text level work**

Name: Date:

Use this frame to record
your acknowledgements.

Acknowledgements

● Teachers' Notes

✓ This unit addresses the text level requirement for pupils to evaluate their work. This is allied to the reading comprehension text level requirement to evaluate texts by seeing how different sources treat the same information.

✓ **Resources** For initial work, before pupils evaluate their own writing, it would be ideal to have two versions of information on the same subject. These might for instance be two versions of the Fire of London (or an item relevant to their current studies in history) or two explanatory texts concerning the water cycle or how to care for a certain type of pet. To complete this, pupils will also need the pieces of writing they did for Units 18 (recording acknowledgements) and 17 (estate agents' details).

✓ **Sheet B** An instructional sheet suitable for group use. It introduces the tasks to be completed on sheets C and D.

✓ **Sheet C** This sheet includes a frame for the evaluation of a selection of the pieces of writing done by pupils for Unit 18. (The pieces of writing, not the acknowledgements.) You will need to select about four pieces of writing and ask the children to decide which of these they consider the best. It is important to introduce this task in such a way that it is a positive experience for those children who have offered their work for evaluation.

✓ **Sheet D** This is a writing frame in which children evaluate their own pieces of writing from Unit 17. They should be encouraged to comment on what they consider to be particularly successful about their work, as well as saying what they would be able to improve on if asked to repeat the task.

Use this box to write your own notes ready for the next time you use this unit.

Name: Date:

It is important to be able to evaluate your work.

❖   You have already evaluated two texts to decide which of them you thought was the better. You have looked at how well each piece fitted the purpose for which it was written, how well it was presented and whether it was appropriate for its audience.

❖   Now you are going to evaluate work done by yourself or your classmates.

❖   Your teacher will ask some of you to allow the writing you did for Unit 18 to be evaluated. Only agree to this if you feel confident about your work.

❖   When the teacher has three or four pieces of work on the same subject, you will be asked to evaluate them carefully and decide which is the most successful for the purpose.

❖   Use Sheet C for writing down your reasons for making your selection. You may not have selected the same piece of writing as another pupil has, but that does not matter. The important aspect of this work is that you are able to write clear reasons for the choice you have made.

✎   Your next evaluation task concerns the Estate Agency details you wrote as part of Unit 17.

✎   You can look at your details again and think about how well they would have helped the sale of the property.

✎   Use the writing frame on Sheet D to evaluate your work. Write down what you think was best about it and what you would change if you had to do the Estate Agency task again.

● **Text level work**

Name: Date:

Which piece of writing best suited its purpose?

Give reasons for your answer.

● Text level work

Name: Date:

... the 'estate agency' home details you wrote.

Use this frame to evaluate ...

● Teachers' Notes

✓   This unit contains some vocabulary based tasks that are word level requirements that link particularly closely to text level work.

✓   **Resources**   An example of a text containing technical vocabulary. This is to read through with the class and pick out the technical vocabulary, thus ensuring that pupils understand the term 'technical vocabulary'.

✓   **Sheet B**   This sheet contains some of the literacy related technical vocabulary encountered by pupils during this year. It can be used to assess their knowledge or, of course, to work on their dictionary skills. This sheet stands alone, and could be used at any time during the term.

✓   **Sheet C**   This sheet asks pupils to collect the technical vocabulary that they might meet in school during the course of the week.

✓   **Sheet D**   This sheet builds upon the previous one by asking pupils to arrange the technical vocabulary they have collected into alphabetical order and to put a definition by each word. Another way to use this sheet would be for the class to share the technical vocabulary that has been collected during the week. Each pupil could take responsibility for words that begin with a particular letter. In this way, with a sheet for each letter of the alphabet, a class word bank of technical vocabulary could be started.

Use this box to write your own notes ready for the next time you use this unit.

Name: Date:

Test your knowledge.

Write a good definition for each of the following words.

✎   Discuss your ideas with your friends before writing your definition.

✎   You may use a dictionary if you get stuck.

vocabulary _____
_____

key words _____
_____

onomatopoeia _____
_____

comma _____
_____

simile _____
_____

legend _____
_____

evaluate _____
_____

subheading _____
_____

non-fiction _____
_____

● **Word level work**

Name: Date:

During any week at school …

… you are likely to learn some new technical vocabulary.

✎ Throughout this week jot down any new technical vocabulary you meet, on the pad below.

Make sure you know the meaning of each word.

Name: Date:

✐   Use the frame below to arrange your technical vocabulary into alphabetical order.

✐   Write a clear definition beside each word.

● **Teachers' Notes**

✓ This unit contains work on the text level requirement to write from another character's point of view.
This work is further developed in Unit 22.

✓ **Resources** One or more versions of 'The Three Billy-goats Gruff' story. Use these to show how, in the story, the three goats are always portrayed as the heroes whilst the troll is the villain. Discuss with the pupils how the troll might feel about the incident.

✓ **Sheet B** This is an instructional sheet suitable for class or group use.

✓ **Sheet C** This is a writing frame for writing the story from the point of view of the Billy-goats - as remembered by Little Billy-goat.

✓ **Sheet D** This is a writing frame for writing the story from the point of view of the troll.

✓ You may wish all children to do both tasks, or you may wish some pupils to be goats whilst others are trolls.

Use this box to write your own notes ready for the next time you use this unit.

Name: Date:

❖   You are sure to know the story of The Three Billy-goats Gruff. It's a traditional tale that most children first hear when they are very young.

❖   Little Billy-goat Gruff is now an adult and has children who often ask to hear the story of how their dad beat the wicked troll.

❖   The troll is very old now and his grandchildren also like being told stories. They sometimes ask for the story of how the wicked goats tricked Grandad out of his own lovely dark damp home.

❖   Do you think the stories would be very similar?

❖   If not, why not?

❖   Discuss your ideas with your friends.

✎   Use Sheet C to write the story as if you are the goat that has grown up and is telling the story to his children.

✎   Use Sheet D to write the story as if you are the troll telling the tale to his grandchildren.

✎   Both Sheets C and D have spaces for numbers, as either of the stories might take more than one page.

Enjoy imagining how your character would have told the story.

● **Text level work**

Name: Date:

Use this frame for
the goat's tale.

Name: Date:

Use this frame to write the troll's tale.

_____

● **Teachers' Notes**

✓ As with Unit 21, this unit contains work on the text level requirement to write from another character's point of view.
In this case the work is based on a well-known fable and asks pupils to write letters. The frames provided are unlined. Letter writing guideline sheets are to be found at the back of this publication.

✓ **Resources** At least one version of the 'Sun and Wind' fable.

✓ **Sheet B** Instructional sheet suitable for class or group use.

✓ **Sheet C** Frame for letter to newspaper from the 'man' subjected to the argument between the sun and the wind.

✓ **Sheet D** This is a frame for a letter from either the sun or the wind explaining what happened from their point of view.

Use this box to write your own notes ready for the next time you use this unit.

Name: Date:

Literacy Times

Freak weather a mystery

Meteorologists confirmed today that they are unable to explain last Wednesday's unusual weather conditions. A spokesman said, "We had no reason to believe that any bad weather was on the way." The strange, and so far unexplained, weather was confined to one small village, which experienced alternate bursts of hot sunshine and gale force winds. If anyone knows anything more about this phenomenon, please write in and let us know.

❖ Make sure you have read Aesop's Fable of 'The Sun and The Wind'.

❖ Now think about writing a letter to the newspaper about the strange weather.

✍ To write as the person at whom the weather was aimed, use Sheet C to write a letter about what happened to you.

✍ To write as either the sun or the wind, use Sheet D for your letter.

✍ Remember whichever character you are, you will look upon yourself as the 'hero' or 'heroine' of the story.

Name: Date:

If you are writing as the 'victim' of the story ...

... use this frame.

● Text level work

Name: Date:

If you are writing as the sun or the wind …

… use this frame.

● Teachers' Notes

✓ This unit is designed to cover the text level requirement to record thoughts on reading materials. In this instance it is done through a mini reading journal that could be used by others to guide their book choices.

✓ **Resources** None beyond the reading books that pupils will normally have access to.

✓ **Sheet B/C** These should be copied to form one double-sided piece of paper that can be folded to form a simple A5 booklet. This booklet can be used to record ideas and reflections on three books as they are read.

✓ **Sheet D** This is an instructional sheet suitable for class or group use. It needs to be considered <u>before</u> the booklet is completed.

✓ It is important to stress to pupils that detailed answers are required in each of the answer boxes in their booklets. Without appropriate detail the booklets will be of little use to other class members who may consult them as an aid to making informed reading choices.

✓ In the situation where two or more children have read and recorded their ideas concerning the same book, an excellent extension activity is to ask them to discuss their thoughts on the book and to then formulate a joint response on it.

Use this box to write your own notes ready for the next time you use this unit.

Reading Journal

Name: _____

This journal concerns the three books listed below.

① Title _____
   Author _____

② Title _____
   Author _____

③ Title _____
   Author _____

Use the instructions on sheet D to help you complete this journal.

3 Title _____

   Author _____

Main characters

Plot outline

Ending

Recommendation

☆ ☆ ☆ ☆ ☆

● **Text level work**

1

Title _____

Author _____

Main characters

Plot outline

Ending

Recommendation

☆ ☆ ☆ ☆ ☆

Title _____

Author _____

Main characters

Plot outline

Ending

Recommendation

☆ ☆ ☆ ☆ ☆

2

Name: Date:

❖ You will be given a mini-journal to use whilst you are reading your next three books.

❖ On the front of the journal you will write the titles and authors of your books. You will of course also write your own name.

❖ Make sure the front cover is as well presented as possible to ensure that others will want to read your journal.

❖ You may wish to choose books by the same author as this will help you to get to know the way that author writes, and whether the plots have similar themes.

❖ You may wish to choose books by three authors whose books you have never tried before so that you learn whether you like the work of a particular person.

Completing The Details

Main Characters

In this box you should insert the names of the main characters and some important details about their characters, e.g. Mrs Bloggs - a friendly character to whom some very surprising things happen during the story.

Plot Outline

Give a brief plot outline without giving away anything that will spoil the book for others. You can see whether your own predictions about the outcome of the story were correct. Do not say what those predictions might have been though.

Ending

Use this box to say whether you felt the ending was satisfactory. Did the author resolve the plot fully, or might there be a follow-up book you need to read? Do not write anything that could spoil the enjoyment of the book for the next reader.

Recommendation

Use this box to say whether you would recommend this book to others to read, and if so why, and if not why not. Make your comments interesting and meaningful.

Star Rating

1 = Not enjoyed. 2 = Not a bad book.   3 = Quite an enjoyable read.

4 = A very enjoyable book. 5 = One of the best books I have read.

● Teachers' Notes

✓ This unit concerns the text level requirement to write in the style of an author.

✓ **Resources** Books by a selection of appropriate well-known authors. You may wish to limit this to just one or two, or you may have a greater number.

✓ **Sheet B** This is an instructional sheet suitable for group or class use. It introduces the task and outlines how it should be completed. Within this it explains how to use Sheets C and D.

✓ **Sheet C** This sheet is used as a prompt sheet to help pupils to investigate characteristics of a particular author's style of writing.

✓ **Sheet D** This is a writing frame to be used to present the piece of writing produced.

✓ This unit leaves you to decide whether you wish the pupils to add a piece to an existing book, or to write a completely separate story in the style of a particular author.

Use this box to write your own notes ready for the next time you use this unit.

❖   You are going to look at the books of one particular author. Your teacher may tell you which author you will be thinking about, or you may be given a choice of authors.

❖   Your task will be to produce a piece of writing in the same style as that author. You may have to add a bit to one of their books, or write a whole new story in their style.

❖   When you know which author you are working on, you will need to read at least two of his/her books.

❖   Try to think about what features of the author's writing that make it quite different from that of any other author.

✎   Discuss your ideas with a few classmates who are doing work on the same author.

✎   Now use Sheet C to help you to think further about the style of your chosen author.

✎   The questions on Sheet C need only to be answered in note form, or with key words or phrases.

✎   When you have answered those questions you will be ready to plan and write your own work in the style of that author.

✎   Use Sheet D to present your finished text .

<u>Extra Activity</u>

Does the same illustrator do the pictures in all of your chosen author's books? If so, could you illustrate your text in that style?

● **Text level work**

Name: _____ Date: _____

If you can answer these questions you will know how your chosen author writes.

How many main characters are in each book? _____

Are there any similarities between the characters? (Perhaps they are mainly animals, children, families or monsters) _____
_____

Do the stories have similar settings? _____
_____

Does he/she write in chapters? _____
_____

If so, are they long or short chapters? _____
_____

Does each chapter end with a cliff-hanger? _____
_____

Does the author use a fairly predictable plot line, or are there some surprising twists and turns in the story? _____
_____

Does the author describe people or places in great detail, or is much of the description left to the imagination? _____
_____

Is there much dialogue written? _____
_____

Can you find any particular words or phrases that the author seems fond of using? _____
_____

Are there any other things that you think are a particular feature of the author's writing? _____

Now you are ready to write in the style of the author.

Name: Date:

Writing in the style of _____

NB   **These teachers' notes cover Units 25 and 26 - there are no additional notes for Unit 26.**

✓   These units concern the text level writing requirement to use performance poems as models for pupils to produce their own poems. This work is also closely linked to the reading comprehension requirement to read and rehearse poetry for performance.

✓   **Resources**   No extra resources strictly necessary to fulfil the above requirements, but any extra poems suitable for performance, particularly those by the poets featured in Units 25 and 26, would be beneficial.

✓   **Sheet B (Unit 25)** 'Topsy-Turvy World'; poem by William Brighty Rands. Suitable for performance and as starting model for writing a poem that incorporates features of other well-known poems. Ideal for extra illustrations.

✓   **Sheet C (Unit 25)** Four poems by Christina Rossetti. These too are suitable for performance and as models for poetry writing. As models they could lead to poems with similes, poems with questions and answers, and riddles as poems.

✓   **Sheet D (Unit 25)** Gardening Lore by Juliana Horatia Ewing. This poem was provided for performing, and as a starting point for a 'rules' poem.

✓   **Sheet A (Unit 26)** Johnny Head-in-Air by Dr Heinrich Hoffmann. All the poems Hoffman wrote were aimed at providing a light-hearted way to warn young children of the dangers in life. Any of his poems would be excellent for performance and are a very good starting point for poetry writing. Young children of today could be told amusing cautionary tales in the form of poetry to warn them of the dangers of traffic, strangers, electricity and many other things that were not an issue in the 19th century.

✓   **Sheet B (Unit 26)** Two poems by Robert Louis Stevenson. As models for poetry writing, both poems give a little insight into an idealised view of life in the 19th century, as do many other of Stevenson's poems. 'From a Railway Carriage' is also a good model for very rhythmic poetry. Children could write a modern poem called 'From my Car Window' or 'From an Aeroplane'.

✓   **Sheet C (Unit 26)** Instructional sheet for writing poetry based on whichever poems have been used for performance. This sheet also has a notepad for jotting ideas for own poems.

✓   **Sheet D (Unit 26)** Writing frame for presentation of completed poem.

Name: Date:

Read this poem with expression.

Either the verse or the chorus would give you good ideas for writing your own poem.

This poem was written by a poet called William Brighty Rands. He was born in 1823 and died in 1882.

The poem is quite humorous and has one verse and a chorus. See how many traditional rhymes you can spot in the chorus.

Topsy-Turvy World

If the butterfly courted the bee,
And the owl the porcupine;
If churches were built in the sea
And three times one was nine;
If the pony rode his master,
If the buttercups ate the cows,
If the cat had the dire disaster
To be worried, sir, by the mouse;
If mamma, sir, sold the baby
To a gypsy for half a crown;
If a gentleman, sir, was a lady -
The world would be Upside-Down!
If any or all of these wonders
Should ever come about,
I should not consider them blunders,
For I should be Inside-Out!

CHORUS

Ba-ba blackwool
Have you any sheep?
Yes sir, a pack full,
Creep, mouse, creep!
Four-and-twenty little maids
Hanging out the pie,
Out jumped the honey-pot,
Guy Fawkes, Guy!
Cross latch, cross-latch,
Sit and spin the fire,
When the pie was opened,
The bird was on the brier!

These short poems are by Christina Rossetti.

Christina Rossetti lived from 1830 to 1894 and wrote poems for both children and adults. These poems are all quite different in many ways, but they have one similarity; they all rhyme.

What Are Heavy?
What are heavy? Sea-sand and sorrow;
What are brief? Today and tomorrow;
What are frail? Spring blossoms and youth;
What are deep? The ocean and truth.

Comparisons
Hope is like a harebell trembling from its birth,
Love is like a rose the joy of all the earth;
Faith is like a lily lifted high and white,
Love is like a lovely rose the world's delight;
Harebells and sweet lilies show a thornless growth,
But the rose with all its thorns excels them both.

A Riddle
There is one that has a head without an eye,
And there's one that has an eye without a head.
You may find the answer if you try;
And when all is said,
Half the answer hangs upon a thread.

Flint
An emerald is as green as grass;
A ruby red as blood;
A sapphire shines as blue as heaven;
A flint lies in the mud.

A diamond is a brilliant stone,
To catch the world's desire.
An opal holds a fiery spark,
But a flint holds fire.

Can you find more poems by Christina Rossetti?

Juliana Horatia Ewing lived from 1841 until 1885.

She wrote the poem presented below.

Gardening Lore

Every child who has gardening tools
Should learn by heart these gardening rules:

He who owns a gardening spade,
Should be able to dig the depth of its blade.

He who owns a gardening rake,
Should know what to leave and what to take.

He who owns a gardening hoe,
Must be sure how he means his strokes to go.

But he who owns a gardening fork,
May make it do all the other tools' work.

Though to shift, or to pot, or annex what you can,
A trowel's the tool for child, woman or man.

'Twas the bird that sits in the medlar-tree,
Who sang these gardening laws to me.

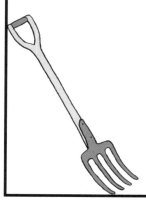

Could you write a poem about rules?

● **Text level work**

Name: Date:

Dr. Heinrich Hoffman was German, and lived from 1809 to 1874.

He wrote poems to encourage children to follow rules and remain safe.

The story of Johnny Head-In-Air

As he trudg'd along to school
It was always Johnny's rule
To be looking at the sky
And the clouds that floated by.
But what just before him lay, in his way,
Johnny never thought about;
So that everyone cried out –
"Look at little Johnny there,
Little Johnny Head-in-Air!"

Running just in Johnny's way,
Came a little dog one day;
Johnny's eyes were still astray
Up on high,
In the sky;
And he never heard them cry -
"Johnny, mind, the dog is nigh!" -
Bump! Dump!
Down they fell with such a thump!
Dog and Johnny in a lump!

Once with head as high as ever,
Johnny walked beside the river.
Johnny watch'd the swallows trying
Which was cleverest at flying.
Oh! what fun
Johnny watched the bright round sun
Going in and coming out.
This was all he thought about.
So he strode and only think,
To the river's very brink
Where the bank was high and steep
And the river very deep
And the fishes in a row stand to see him
coming so.

One step more!
Oh sad to tell!
Headlong in poor Johnny fell
And the fishes in dismay,
Wagg'd their tails and ran away.
There lay Johnny on his face,
With his nice red writing case;
But, as they were passing by,
Two big men had heard him cry -
And with sticks, the two big men
Hooked poor Johnny out again.

Oh! you should have seen him shiver,
When they pulled him from the river.
He was in a sorry plight!
Dripping wet and such a fright!
Wet all over everywhere,
Clothes, and arms and face and hair -
Johnny never will forget
What it is to be so wet!
And the fishes, one, two, three,
Are come back again you see;
Up they came the moment after,
To enjoy the fun and laughter.
Each popp'd out his little head
And to tease poor Johnny, said -
"Silly little Johnny, look,
You have lost your writing book!"

Name: Date:

The poems of R.L. Stevenson paint an idealised picture of life in the late 19th century.

Read the first poem below, paying particular attention to the rhythm.

From a Railway Carriage

Faster than fairies, faster than witches,
Bridges and houses, hedges and ditches;
And charging along like troops in a battle,
All through the meadows the horses and
cattle:
All of the sights of the hill and the plain
Fly as thick as driving rain;
And ever again, in the wink of an eye,
Painted stations whistle by.

Here is a child who clambers and
scrambles,
All by himself and gathering brambles;
Here is a tramp who stands and gazes;
And there is the green for stringing the
daisies!
Here is a cart run away in the road
Lumping along with man and load;
Here is a mill and there is a river:
Each a glimpse and gone for ever!

The Land of Counterpane

When I was sick and lay a-bed,
I had two pillows at my head,
And all my toys beside me lay
To keep me happy all the day.

And sometimes for an hour or so
I watched my leaden soldiers go,
With different uniforms and drills,
Among the bed-clothes, through the hills;

And sometimes sent my ships in fleets
All up and down among the sheets;
Or brought my trees and houses out,
And planted cities all about.

I was the giant great and still
That sits upon the pillow-hill;
And sees before him, dale and plain,
The pleasant land of counterpane.

What is a **counterpane**?

What do you use instead of a counterpane?

● **Text level work**

Name: Date:

Now you have had the chance to choose a poem for performance ....

... you can use it to be a starting point for writing a poem of your own.

✎ Look carefully at the poems provided. Each of them has particular features that give it its character.

✎ There is a poem that lists rules, one with questions and answers, one with a very clear rhythm, one to warn children that they should look where they are going, a riddle and one that makes us think of other traditional rhymes. There are examples of similes, there is rhyme and there are other structural patterns for you to notice.

✎ Choose one of the poems and, in the box below, note all the features that you can find.

_____

_____

_____

_____

_____

✎ Share your ideas with a friend.

✎ Now plan and write a poem using the features of your chosen poem.

✎ Remember all you know about writing poetry. Revise and improve your work over two or three writing sessions.

✎ Begin to jot your initial ideas in the box below.

_____

_____

_____

_____

_____

Name: Date:

Present your poem here.

Illustrate it with care.

● **Teachers' Notes**

✓ This unit contains work on the text level requirement to produce a piece of discursive writing about a novel or story.

✓ The unit asks children to write a book review for a magazine.

✓ **Resources** Books about which to write.
You may prefer all children to produce work on the same book, perhaps one that has been read by the class, or you may wish each child to work on a different text.

✓ **Sheet B** This is a sheet of instructions and is suitable for class or group use.

✓ **Sheet C** This is a frame in which to present the final piece of writing.

✓ **Sheet D** This is a frame suitable for presenting handwriting of each pupil's favourite extract from the book.

Use this box to write your own notes ready for the next time you use this unit.

● Text level work

Name: Date:

You are going to write a magazine article …

… reviewing a book you have read recently.

Task One

✐ Imagine you have been asked, by a magazine publisher, to review a book you have read.

✐ It is important to write about the book in a way that includes facts about the book, your opinion of it and the reasons for your opinion.

✐ Remember to include the title and author of the book.

✐ You must include a very brief plot outline and facts about the sort of book it is (e.g. thriller, romance, non-fiction etc.).

✐ Make your writing both interesting and informative.

✐ Conclude your article with an overall opinion of the book and, if appropriate, a recommendation for others to read it too.

✐ Draft your article in rough first and ask a friend to read and evaluate it.

✐ When you have made any amendments or improvements to your draft, you can present your final piece of writing on the Sheet C display frame.

Task Two

✐ Choose a short extract from the book you have reviewed.

✐ Present this extract in your very best handwriting on Sheet D. You may add a small illustration if appropriate.

● **Text level work**

Name: Date:

Write your article on the frame below.

Literacy Times Magazine

Book review by _____

Name: Date:

Use your very best handwriting to write an extract from the book.

Use guidelines to keep your work neat.

● Teachers' Notes

✓ This unit contains work on the text level requirement to write a letter for a real purpose. This may be a letter from an individual or from a group.

✓ **Resources** Samples of letters sent to magazines or newspapers. These can be used to select effective, appropriate words and phrases for use in pupils' own letters. These resources will also enable you to cover the text level reading requirement to read and evaluate letters.

Suitable subjects for a letter with a real purpose might include:
~ a matter of local topical interest (new road building, local conservation issues, etc.);
~ national issues including political issues (perhaps concerning education or health);
~ environmental concerns.

✓ **Sheet B** This is an instructional sheet suitable for group or class use.

✓ **Sheet C** This is a frame for planning letters and includes space for children to write down particularly effective phrases.

✓ **Sheet D** This is a writing frame for the presentation of the final version of a letter.

Use this box to write your own notes ready for the next time you use this unit.

Name: Date:

You are going to write an important letter.

It will actually be sent off.

🖉 You will be working on a letter that you have already decided on with your teacher.

🖉 You may be composing your letter on your own, with a partner or as part of a small group.

🖉 Before you draft your letter you will need to plan the ideas and arguments you wish to present.

🖉 You will also need to look at examples of other letters so that you can pick out some powerful phrases or sentences to use.

🖉 When you are looking at examples of letters, try to note what sort of formal language is used.

🖉 When you are planning your letter, remember to use reasoned argument and to back up your ideas with evidence if possible.

🖉 To write a persuasive argument you must always write in an objective and non-threatening way, to ensure your reader remains sympathetic to your ideas.

🖉 Always imagine that you are the person who has received the letter when you read it through to yourself. How would you feel if it had just arrived on your door-mat?

🖉 When you have planned and drafted your letter ask someone else to read it and comment on it.

🖉 You can use Sheet C to help you to plan your letter. On this sheet there is a space for noting the sort of formal language that you have read in the examples you have been shown. There is also a space for noting down the key ideas that you need to include in your letter.

🖉 Use Sheet D to present the final version of your letter ready for posting. It is completely plain, but you can use a letter writing guidelines sheet to help you to present your work well.

🖉 Remember to use the correct formal beginning and ending of your letter.

● **Text level work**

Name: Date:

Use the pad below to write the best phrases from the examples of letters that you have been shown.

Then note down the key ideas that need to be put into your letter.

Name: Date:

Write your letter with great care.

● Teachers' Notes

✓ This unit contains work on the text level requirement to write a commentary on an issue, setting out and justifying a personal view.

✓ **Resources** Whilst there are no extra resources strictly necessary to complete this unit, any books on space, space travel, U.F.O.s, or life in space could be beneficial.
The task around which this unit is based is for each pupil to produce a leaflet presenting their views concerning whether there is life beyond our planet. They must give reasons for their views and use a variety of ways of presenting their ideas.

✓ **Sheet B/C** These should be copied as one double-sided sheet that can be folded to form a leaflet.

✓ **It should be noted that Sheet D should be used before sheets B and C.**

✓ **Sheet D** This is an instructional sheet suitable for class or group use, and gives ideas for the construction of an effective and meaningful leaflet.

Use this box to write your own notes ready for the next time you use this unit.

Is There Life On Other Planets?

by

● **Text level work**

Name: Date:

● **Text level work**

Is there life on other planets?

People have many different ideas about this question.

✐ The leaflet you are going to make is formed from an A4 sheet of paper that is folded into three.

✐ The title page has been started for you with a heading 'Is there life on other planets?' You can choose whether to write YES or NO in the box provided. You may then complete that page with illustrations or comments that make the front of the leaflet eye-catching.

✐ Next you must plan how to complete the remaining five sections of the leaflet. You must justify your view with as much reasoned argument as possible, though of course at present it is completely impossible to actually prove that your opinion is the correct one.

✐ Use the ways you know about to present your ideas in an easy to follow format. You may decide to use lists, bullet points or to present key facts in separate boxes.

✐ Do remember that however you choose to present your ideas, they should be written in a logical order. If possible one idea should be clearly linked to the next.

✐ You may use decoration and illustration to make your leaflet more appealing, and to help clarify your views.

✐ Lastly – Don't forget to name your leaflet.

Does U.F.O stand for 'unidentified flying object'?

No, it stands for 'unexpected falling ostriches'!

✓   This unit contains work on the text level requirement to construct an argument in note form or full text, and to use this to persuade others of a certain point of view.

✓   **Resources**   No extra resources are needed to complete this unit successfully.

✓   The questions posed at the beginning of this unit concern whether children have the automatic right to pocket money or whether it should be earned in some way. Pupils are also asked to consider what they think is an appropriate amount of weekly pocket money, giving reasons for their answer.

✓   They are then asked to list their reasons in note form, and to write a full text on the matter.

✓   They can use their argument to present their case to the class, who can then help to evaluate it. It is important to stress that the way the argument is constructed and presented is what is being evaluated not whether they agree with the conclusions.

✓   **Sheet B**   An instructional sheet, suitable for group or whole class use.

✓   **Sheet C**   A writing frame for presenting the argument in note form.

✓   **Sheet D**   This is a writing frame for the presentation of final, well-constructed arguments written as full texts.

Use this box to write your own notes ready for the next time you use this unit.

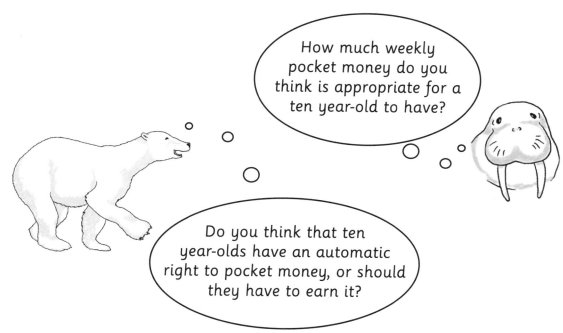

✐   Think about these questions.

✐   You are going to present a well-constructed argument to your classmates to try to persuade them that your point of view is the correct one to have.

✐   You will have clear key points in your argument and you will give reasons for all your ideas.

✐   When thinking about the amount of weekly pocket money that is appropriate, you should give your audience an idea of what the money should have to be spent on.

✐   Make sure the points in your argument are recorded in a logical order.

✐   Use Sheet C to present your argument in note form. A clear concise list of ideas marked with bullet points would be ideal for this.

✐   Use Sheet D to present your argument as a full written text that would be suitable for reading aloud to your classmates.

● Text level work

Name: Date:

Use this frame to construct your argument in note form.

A numbered sequence, or bullet points might help to make it clear.